THE
low carb
COOKBOOK

GINA STEER

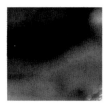 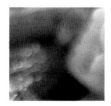 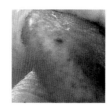 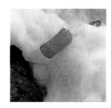  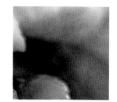

This is a Parragon Publishing Book
First published in 2004

Parragon Publishing
Queen Street House
4 Queen Street
Bath
BA1 1HE
UK

Designed and produced by
THE BRIDGEWATER BOOK COMPANY

Introduction, Nutritional Facts and Analyses: *Charlotte Watts*
Photography: *Clive Bozzard-Hill*
Home Economist: *Philippa Vanstone*
Stylist: *Angela Macfarlane*

The publishers would like to thank the following companies for the loan
of props: *Dartington Crystal, Marlux Mills, Maxwell & Williams, Lifestyle Collections,
Viners & Oneida, Typhoon, and John Lewis.*

Printed in China

ISBN 1-40543-688-3

NOTES FOR THE READER

This book uses imperial, metric, or US cup measurements. Follow the same
units of measurement throughout; do not mix imperial and metric. All spoon
measurements are level, unless otherwise stated: teaspoons are assumed
to be 5 ml and tablespoons are assumed to be 15 ml.

Individual vegetables such as potatoes are medium and pepper is freshly
ground black pepper. Milk used in the recipes is skim or semiskim to help
limit the fat content of the meal. The recipes have been made with
a reduced-fat and -sugar content in accordance with healthy eating guidelines.
However, this means that they will not keep fresh for as long a period of
time as their higher-fat and -sugar alternatives.

Some of the recipes require stock. If you use commercially made bouillon
granules or cubes, these can have a relatively high salt content, so do not
add any further salt. If you make your own stock, keep the fat and salt content
to a minimum. Don't sauté the vegetables before simmering—just simmer the
vegetables, herbs, and meat, poultry, or fish in water and strain. Meat and
poultry stocks should be strained, cooled, and refrigerated before use so that
the fat from the meat rises to the top and solidifies—it can then be easily
removed and this reduces the saturated fat content of the meal. Homemade
stocks should be stored in the refrigerator and used within two days, or frozen
in usable portions and labeled.

Ovens should be preheated to the specified temperature. If using a fan-
assisted oven, check the manufacturer's instructions for adjusting the time
and temperature.

The values of the nutritional analysis for each recipe refer to a single
serving, or a single slice where relevant. They do not include the serving
suggestion. Where a range of portions is given the nutritional analysis figure
refers to the mid-range figure. The calorific value given is in KCal (Kilocalories).
The carbohydrate figure includes starches and sugars, with the sugar value
then given separately. The fat figure is likewise the total fat, with the saturated
part then given separately.

   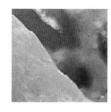  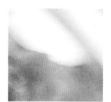

contents

Introduction

There have been several widely adopted "dieting" trends over the last 30–40 years, but none has affected to the same degree the way that people approach weight loss as the high-protein, low-carbohydrate diet made so popular in recent times. The aim of this book is to put the basic principles underlying that weight-loss program into practice in a range of recipes which constitute a sensible eating plan, while avoiding the well-documented health risks hitherto associated with this particular dietary approach.

A significant proportion of people today are showing symptoms and conditions associated with poor blood-sugar control. This is where the levels of sugar or glucose in the blood become too high from consuming too many or inappropriate kinds of carbohydrate, from overuse of stimulants (caffeine, cigarettes, and alcohol) or from an excess of stress. On a day-to-day basis this can lead to weight gain, and also to fatigue, headaches, anxiety, irritability, depression, insomnia, poor memory and concentration, and difficulty coping with stress. This sets up a cycle where a slump of blood sugar after the sudden rush from the food or stimulus causes a craving for something else to lift the blood sugar back up again. This is when people turn to caffeine and sugar, which is what the English tradition of "high tea" was invented for, since the time it was traditionally served, at 4 pm, is when people often experience a blood-sugar slump and feel the need for a "fix."

Continual high blood-sugar levels can have a more serious outcome, leading to high cholesterol, heart disease, obesity, and increasing problems with mental function. People who recognize this blood-sugar cycle may have trouble dealing with carbohydrates and the reason for this lies with insulin—see The Role of Insulin (opposite). In this case, they may be suited to a diet that contains fewer starches and grains, especially if they are also experiencing digestive problems. The best advice is to experiment by omitting these foods and seeing how the body reacts.

Many people find that lowering carbohydrate intake helps them lose weight, but this does not have to involve increasing protein and saturated fat intake to potentially dangerous levels. A diet that prioritizes some lean meat, vegetable proteins, low-sugar vegetables, and beneficial oils can have many far-reaching health benefits, and people often feel generally much cleaner, lighter, and more efficient on this type of diet. But you are the best judge of how you feel, and learning to listen to your body's needs is an important part of becoming healthier. These dietary guidelines can, in any case, help you to manage your weight, in conjunction with a suitable exercise program and a controlled daily calorie intake. The recipes are also delicious, which is a very important factor in sustaining your commitment to a healthy diet.

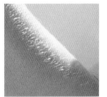

Insulin Sensitivity

Too much insulin can also lead to insulin sensitivity, where the body loses the ability to recognize insulin or to use it properly and consequently levels in the bloodstream remain too high. This has been linked to a condition called Syndrome X, which has associated weight gain, increased body hair, high cholesterol, and heart disease risk.

The Healthy Low-Carbohydrate Approach

Many people have thrived on a diet that is high in protein and without carbohydrates because they have cut out foods that their body has been unable to deal with such as sugars and grains. The problem with massively increasing protein intake is that protein creates acidity in the body, which takes a lot of energy and nutrients to adjust, as it needs to operate in a slightly alkaline state. This response is associated with bone loss, as the alkalizing mineral calcium is taken by the body from bone to buffer this acidity. The high saturated fat foods that are also high protein such as meat and meat products are also associated with heart disease.

Rather than eat too much protein, it is important to consume exactly the right amount, as well as the appropriate types of carbohydrate and fat. Fats and oils are very important for our health but unfortunately in recent times they have been lumped together into one "bad" category. Fat in the form of oils that do not clog the arteries is used to make all cell membranes, keep skin supple, and produce hormones, and is also very efficiently burned as a fuel. Low-carbohydrate diets aim to switch our major fuel-burning substance from carbohydrate to fat, meaning that our bodies store less, burn that which we have stored, and become more efficient. Stored fat is the major heart disease risk, since it can easily reach the arteries. It is important to understand that it is not fat itself which is stored as fat. It is excess carbohydrates that are not used as energy which are converted to fat. This is because the body has no other use for them and insulin has to remove them quickly from the bloodstream.

The Role of Insulin

We have many hormones in the body that raise blood-sugar levels, but only one to lower it—insulin. Our bodies were designed to need high blood sugar only in the advent of danger, in the "fight or flight" response, to provide us with energy in the muscles to deal with an enemy. Stress mimics this response, but in general we don't need to respond so physically to the modern-day anxieties we experience, and so our bodies are left with the task of bringing down these artificially high levels of blood sugar. Along with a diet higher than ever in sugar and carbohydrates, this means that we also have to produce larger amounts of insulin than we should. This can exhaust the pancreas and even eventually lead to Type II diabetes.

This book aims to offer a diet in which, rather than cutting out carbohydrates entirely, you can safely consume them in a way that does not raise your insulin levels and therefore cause weight gain and other adverse symptoms.

The Macronutrients

This is the collective term for carbohydrates, fats, and proteins, so-called because they are much larger molecules than vitamins and minerals. The name "carbohydrate" comes from its components—carbon, hydrogen, and oxygen—and it is burned at an easy rate of 4.1 kilocalories per gram. Fat has the same components yet in a different, insoluble form, but can be broken down to be burned as fuel. We are designed to burn fat in cold climates, as it is a compact, dense form of energy (at 9.4 kilocalories per gram), and save carbohydrates for lean times when we need to store fat to burn later. Proteins contain carbon, hydrogen, oxygen, and also nitrogen, and are needed to form hormones, enzymes, neurotransmitters, antibodies, and structures in the body such as tissues, muscles, bones, skin, and hair. We don't want to burn this as a primary fuel as these structures would be affected, but it can be burned at 5.7 kilocalories per gram.

It is partly the low calorific value of carbohydrates that have led to their popularity in the slimming world, and to the detriment of fats. However, for our ancestors, the calorific values of food, meaning the actual energy that the body can obtain from certain foods, was all-important: it was much more preferable for them to find less food but with a higher calorific content. Compared to modern lifestyles and diet, they expended more energy and ate leaner meats, a greater proportion of "good" fats from nuts, seeds, and fish, hardly any grains and no sugar, except that found in fruit. Many people's bodies are still craving for this dietary approach for optimal health.

Carbohydrates

Carbohydrates are not just found in grains and starches like potatoes and other roots but also in vegetables, fruit, and dairy products. Carbohydrates are made from simple sugars, which can all break down to glucose eventually, but some are in more complicated forms that take longer to release their sugars into the bloodstream. It is now recognized that it is the type of carbohydrate to be consumed that should be considered and the all-important speed in which it breaks down into the glucose components in the body. Vegetables are the most acceptable form in which to eat carbohydrates, as they are also good sources of antioxidant nutrients (vitamins A, C, and E and carotenoids) which protect us from damage from energy production (our vehicle emissions), environmental factors such as sunlight and pollution, and any harmful components in the food that we eat. They will also provide the carbohydrates we need to make our DNA.

Refined carbohydrates or sugars are very simple molecules. What we call "sugar" for cooking and eating is actually sucrose—just two molecules of glucose that offer a very quick supply of sugar to the bloodstream, demanding a high need for insulin that can lead to insulin insensitivity and eventually levels of sugar in the blood that are too high. These are found in processed foods, candies, cakes, soft drinks, fruit juices, and very refined carbohydrates such as white bread, where the bran part of the wheat has been stripped away. This quick release of sugar can be laid down as fat if the equivalent energy is not expended, i.e. if you don't go for a two-mile walk every time you eat a cake.

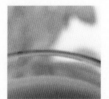

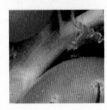

Complex carbohydrates release their sugars more slowly, so are used for energy rather than laid down as fat. These are termed starches. They also contain fiber, which also helps to slow down sugar release and eliminate toxins from the body to help prevent disease. The whole-grain bran part of cereal grains that is removed in white flour and processed foods contains fiber and provides glucose molecules that are bound together in more complex structures. Vegetables and fruit in their natural, raw state provide complex carbohydrates bound in fiber. They therefore take much more time to break down into their simple sugars and provide a more slow and steady release into the bloodstream.

The carbohydrate issue is, however, not as simple as previously thought—see the Glycemic Index (pages 10–11).

Grains

Human beings only began eating grains when they changed from being hunter-gatherers to farmers, which in historical terms was relatively recently. Carbohydrates make up about 90 percent of the world's food supply, the top ten being wheat, corn, rice, barley, soybeans, sugar cane, sorghum, potatoes, oats, and cassava. Of these, half are grains, and it is ironic that many people may find that these affect their blood sugar and insulin levels adversely. Many people have wheat and gluten (the protein in wheat, rye, oats, and barley) intolerance due to them being difficult to digest and because of the mere fact that they are so prevalent in our diets; we were designed to eat a variety of foods over different seasons and can suffer overload from a diet of toast, sandwiches, and cereals. You may

have more of a problem with wheat or other grains than other carbohydrates and you should suspect an intolerance if you have digestive problems, headaches, fatigue, bloating, and joint pain on top of the other symptoms of poor blood-sugar balance. You can try eliminating these grains to monitor symptoms, but this can be confusing as the effects of an intolerance can sometimes manifest days after eating the food—consult a nutritionist for further advice. If you are cutting out grains, eat a range of vegetables, nuts, and beans to obtain appropriate amounts of fiber and B vitamins.

Fiber

Fiber can either be soluble or insoluble fiber. Each has its different properties, so both are important in the diet and a balance is needed. Fiber helps to level out blood sugar by slowing down digestion and the release of sugar from food. Aim for 35 grams per day to balance blood sugar, lower cholesterol levels, cleanse the colon of toxins, and to help prevent heart disease.

Soluble fiber tends to be found in fruit and vegetables, especially apples, citrus fruits, carrots, cherries, avocados, beet, dried apricots, and prunes, and also some seed husks such as linseed, oat bran, and psyllium husks, which many people take to counter constipation. It helps digestion by absorbing water and softening stools, and this can help lower cholesterol. You should aim to obtain soluble fiber by eating as many different vegetables as possible, as well as some dark fruits and berries.

Insoluble fiber remains undigested and so clears the digestive system, prevents constipation, lessens the incidence of colon and rectal cancer, and speeds up the elimination of waste from the body. It is found in brown rice (the fiber is removed when processed to white), rye bread and crackers, lentils, asparagus, Brussels sprouts, cabbage, other whole-grains, and fibrous vegetables. When eating smaller amounts of grains, you need to compensate by eating more of these fibrous vegetables.

Vegetables and fruit contain cellulose, an insoluble plant fiber that contains little sugar, but it is important to remember that when cooked these become more readily broken down

into sugars. This is why vegetables such as carrots, bell peppers, and parsnips taste sweeter the longer they are cooked. Raw vegetables are much more beneficial on the whole. Some fruit can be eaten as a good source of nutrients and soluble fiber, but choose less sweet varieties such as grapes, pineapple, and bananas and darker, tarter fruits that release sugar less quickly such as berries, cherries, plums, and sharp, green apples instead of sweet, red ones. Fruit juices are already broken down into more simple sugars and have had the fiber removed. Your taste buds can guide you—think, for instance, how much sweeter white bread tastes than brown; if you chew a piece for a few minutes, you will taste pure maltose, the sugar that is its main component. See the Glycemic Index on pages 10–11 for further guidance.

Fats

If you lower your intake of the carbohydrates that can cause the accumulation of body fat, make sure that you include the beneficial oils and essential fats that can produce energy, lower cholesterol, and help blood-sugar regulation. It is important to know which oils are best and how they should be used.

Saturated fats tend to be from animal sources, such as butter and meat fats. Solid at room temperature, they can form in the same way in the body. If eaten in high amounts, they can clog arteries and add to the risk of heart disease. Combined with sugars, they can be laid down as fat. Foods containing both, such as pastries, are the main culprits of weight gain.

Monounsaturated fats are vegetable in origin and those traditionally eaten in Mediterranean countries, namely olive, almond, hazelnut, peanut, and avocado oils. They contain a fatty acid called oleic acid or omega-9 and remain liquid at room temperature but begin to solidify when refrigerated. These have been found to have a neutral effect on blood cholesterol, although an excess can raise fat levels in the blood. The exception is olive oil, which has been shown actually to reduce blood cholesterol. However, this effect is thought to be caused by unique active components rather than the monounsaturated fat content. These are less damaged by heat than oils that stay liquid at room temperature and therefore can be used for cooking at low to medium temperatures.

Polyunsaturated fatty acids are always liquid and contain the essential fatty acids, the omega-6 oils, that help to produce localized hormones in the body, which are important for blood-sugar and cholesterol regulation and heart health. These include sesame, soy, sunflower-seed, walnut, pumpkin, and hemp oils. They are termed "essential" because they are crucial to body functions and must be consumed as they cannot be made in the body. Saturated fats can actually stop essential fats being used at a cellular level. These should be used cold for dressings and dips as they are very susceptible to damage from heat.

With both polyunsaturated and monounsaturated fats, eating the nuts, seeds, and vegetables from which these oils are produced can also play a vital role in blood-sugar management. For example, avocados contain not only beneficial oils but high levels of nutrients and soluble fiber, and plant sterols (types of fat) which help to reduce bad cholesterol. Although avocados, olives, nuts, and seeds also contain some saturated fats and should be eaten in moderation, they provide omega-6 oils, vitamin E, vitamins B_3 and B_6, zinc, and magnesium, which all aid blood-sugar management.

Omega-3 oils are those found in oily fish such as salmon, tuna, herring, mackerel, trout, and sardines. Like the omega-6 oils, these are essential fatty acids and are crucial to our health. Much research has shown how important these are for heart health and they should be eaten 3–4 times a week, in variety. Both omega-3 and omega-6 oils protect parts of the body that are rich in fats—the eyes, kidneys, and liver—as well as the circulation from the heart. For vegetarians, hemp, pumpkin, soy, and walnut oils contain some omega-3 oils but are higher in omega-6. Omega-3 and omega-6 should be eaten in a one-to-one ratio and flax or linseed can be added to food as a source of omega-3 oils.

Proteins

Proteins are the major source of building materials for the body. They can also be used as a source of energy that is released very slowly. They are therefore very good for blood-sugar management and can slow down sugar release into the bloodstream if eaten with less complex carbohydrates.

Many people do not eat enough proteins to sustain the body's structural needs, especially at breakfast time when the body is setting up its supply for the demands of the day. Caution should be taken, however, not to obtain these mainly from high-fat sources such as meats, but additionally from eggs, low-fat dairy products, and vegetable sources such as peas and beans, and in small amounts from other vegetables such as broccoli, cauliflower, and asparagus. Too much protein can create excess acidity in the body. Protein requirements can be as low as 35 g for smaller women to up to 200 g a day for a heavily exercising athlete, but generally proteins should account for 30 percent of your daily calorie intake. You may have a higher need if you exercise often, but you then need to counter this extra acidity with more vegetables to alkalize your body.

The Glycemic Index

Research into sugars and their release into the bloodstream has found that some foods behave in a surprising way when introduced into the body. It is no longer enough just to distinguish between simple sugars and complex carbohydrates. As we are unable to predict how a food will act by its sugar and starch content alone, the Glycemic Index has been drawn up to compare the release of sugar into the bloodstream that foods create against a measure of 100 for glucose. In the table on the right, foods are categorized into high, medium, and low. High (more than 70) means that sugars are released very quickly, near to the speed of glucose itself. These foods should not be eaten on their own as this can cause a quick increase of blood sugar. They can, however, be eaten in small amounts at the same time as a food with a low score (under 55). This would equal a combined score in the medium range (55–70) and a good control of blood sugar. You should aim to include as many foods in the low range as possible for the best blood-sugar control and include those in the medium or high categories only with protein or other low-GI foods.

A low-GI diet can help to increase the body's sensitivity to insulin, so that the insulin you have works more effectively and you are less likely to become insensitive to it. A low-GI diet can also, in conjunction with a low-saturated fat diet, help to keep blood fats low, and therefore reduce heart disease-related risks.

Knowing the GI values of foods is very useful in keeping your actual carbohydrate load in check as you may be getting more sugar straight into the bloodstream than you expected from certain foods. For instance, note that corn flakes and parsnips have very high scores and should be eaten very sparingly with foods that bring the score down overall. Proteins and oils are not included in the Glycemic Index as they are known to be low-GI foods since they do not contain carbohydrates. They can, therefore, be eaten

Low-GI Foods—below 55

Fruit and Fruit Juices

Cherries	22
Grapefruit	25
Dried apricots	31
Pears	37
Apples	38
Plums	39
Apple juice	41
Peaches	42
Oranges	44
Grapes	46
Pineapple juice	46
Grapefruit juice	48
Orange juice	52
Kiwifruit	53
Banana	54

Vegetables

Broccoli	10
Cabbage	10
Lettuce	10
Mushrooms	10
Raw onions	10
Raw red bell peppers	10
Raw carrots	49
Sweet potatoes	54

Grains

Pearl barley	31
Rye	34
Brown basmati rice	52

Breads

Mixed grain bread	48
Pumpernickel rye bread	50

Pasta

Vermicelli	35
Linguine	42
Instant noodles	47

Bakery Products

Sponge cake (made with egg)	46

Breakfast Cereals

Bran cereal	42

Dairy

Lowfat yogurt	14
Whole milk	27
Skim milk	27
Lowfat fruit yogurt	33
Custard	43

Legumes

Soybeans	14
Red split lentils	18
Green lentils	29
Canned chickpeas	42
Canned pinto beans	45
Green peas	48

Medium-GI Foods—55–70

Fruit and Fruit Juices

Mangoes	56
Golden raisins	56
Apricots	57
Raisins	64
Pineapple	66

Vegetables

Corn	55
New potatoes	57
Beet	64
Boiled or mashed potatoes	70

Grains

White basmati rice	58
Buckwheat	55
Brown rice	55

Breads

White pita bread	58
Hamburger bun	61
Rye flour bread	64
High-fiber wheat bread	68
Whole-wheat bread	69

Pasta

Durum wheat spaghetti	55

Bakery Products

Pastry	59
Muffin	62
Croissant	67
Crumpet	69

Breakfast Cereals

Granola	56
Porridge	61
Spun wheat biscuit	69
Wheat biscuits	70

Cookies

Oatmeal cookies	55
Tea cookies	55
Digestive cookies	59
Shortbread	64

Savory Cookies

Wheat thins	67

Dairy

Ice cream	61

Sugars

High-fruit jelly	55
Honey	58
Table sugar	64

Candies and Snacks

Popcorn	55

Beverages

Orange cordial	66
Fizzy orange	68

High-GI Foods—above 70

Fruit and Fruit Juices

Watermelon	72

Vegetables

Rutabaga	72
French fries	75
Pumpkin	75
Baked potatoes	85
Cooked carrots	85
Parsnips	97

Grains

White rice	88

Breads

White bagel	72
White wheat bread	78
Gluten-free bread	90
French baguette	95

Bakery Products

Doughnuts	76
Waffles	76

Breakfast Cereals

Wheat bran flakes with added dried fruit	71
Puffed wheat	74
Crisped rice	82
Corn flakes	83

Savory Cookies and Crackers

Water biscuits	71
Rice cakes	77
Puffed crispbread	81

Candies and Snacks

Corn tortillas	74
Jelly beans	80
Pretzels	81
Dates	99

Beverages

High-glucose sports drinks	95

Legumes

Fava beans	79

with the high-GI foods to slow down sugar release, for instance lean chicken with parsnips or low-GI nuts with corn flakes. This approach has been used in this book to create low- and medium-GI recipes that may still contain small amounts of high-GI foods but will not raise blood-sugar levels beyond the "normal" range by combining for average scores. Some "treat" foods such as ice cream and cookies have surprisingly low GI scores, but this is often due to their high fat content and they should still be eaten sparingly.

General Dietary Advice

Eat as many raw fruits and vegetables and fresh vegetable juices as you can where practical. This ensures a slow release of sugar into the bloodstream, and the intake of beneficial insoluble fiber and nutrient-dense foods. Lightly cook vegetables and make these the mainstay of your carbohydrate intake, paying attention to the GI scores on pages 10–11.

A healthy low-carbohydrate diet minimizes the inclusion of foods high in starchy carbohydrates (potatoes and cooked root vegetables), and grains and cereals (wheat, oats, bread, pasta, noodles, couscous, and bulgur wheat). Beans, peas and pulses contain starchy carbohydrates but also good amounts of protein and fiber and so should be included in your diet.

The most important factor is to avoid foods that are high in sugary carbohydrates—these include the usual demons such as chocolate, cookies, muffins, cakes, and so on.

Foods that contain nutrients needed for blood-sugar balance (zinc, magnesium, vitamins B_3, B_6, and C) are nuts, seeds, fish, dark green vegetables, brassicas, beans, peas, eggs, avocados, oats, onions, and asparagus. These foods are also important for managing cholesterol levels and lowering the risk of heart

disease. Avoiding stimulants (caffeine, alcohol, and cigarettes) helps to eliminate "highs and lows" of blood sugar and reduce sugar cravings.

About the Recipes

When putting together the recipes in this book, practicality and ease were important factors. Choices were made to provide you with an accessible diet that aims to help you feel more healthy and in control of your body. The overall GI score of combinations of foods was considered and a rating of either low or medium has been assigned to each recipe. It makes sense for you to prioritize those that are low and eat the medium ones less often, as they will naturally release sugar into your bloodstream more quickly, even if the carbohydrate content appears to be lower. It is also important to vary your diet and the recipes to ensure a good spread of different nutrients in any given week—you can do this by consulting the nutritional information accompanying each recipe.

A nutritional fact is also provided for each recipe, which highlights the specific health benefits of certain foods, for instance in balancing blood sugar, increasing the uptake of insulin, burning fuel more efficiently, and therefore reducing weight and the risk of heart disease. Foods that are considered to be of particular benefit for blood-sugar balance are blueberries, cinnamon, chicory, onion, beans, garlic, olive oil, nuts, and avocados. These should be included in your diet often, but remember that a variety of foods is paramount to health, to ensure a full range and balance of nutrients.

Some of the recipes include grains such as rice and couscous as accompaniments. If you wish to try eliminating these to monitor health and symptoms, replace them with additional vegetables and beans to ensure that you obtain enough fiber and B vitamins.

The choice of specific varieties of ingredients used in the recipes also takes into account their effect on the release of blood sugar. For instance, if rice is featured, brown rice has been chosen as the best option. In the same way, consideration has been given to the choice of oils and types of fiber and carbohydrates, and this is reflected in the nutritional analyses.

Quick Tomato Sauce

Here is a very useful and versatile recipe for tomato sauce, which is also featured in a couple of the following recipes and can be used as an accompaniment to your own favorite recipes. Simply by adding different fresh herbs, a chopped fresh chili or a dash of balsamic vinegar or wine, the flavor can be adapted to suit whatever dish it accompanies.

SERVES 4–6

1 tbsp olive oil
1–2 garlic cloves, crushed
2 shallots, finely chopped
14 oz/400 g canned chopped tomatoes
⅔ cup vegetable stock
2–3 tsp Worcestershire sauce
salt and pepper
1 tbsp chopped fresh basil

Heat the oil in a pan over medium heat, add the garlic and shallots and cook for 3 minutes, stirring frequently. Stir in the tomatoes with their juice, stock, Worcestershire sauce, and salt and pepper to taste and bring to a boil. Reduce the heat and let simmer for 10–12 minutes, or until a thick sauce consistency is reached. Stir in the basil, taste, adjust the seasoning, and serve. For a smoother sauce, process in a food processor or blender and push through a nylon strainer to remove the seeds, if desired.

Calories 44.4   Protein 1.7g   Carbohydrates 2.5g
Sugars 3.6g   Fat 0g   Saturated Fat 0g   GI Medium

We have included a Desserts & Baking section, which may seem a contradiction in terms, but the recipes are relatively low GI and use very little actual sugar. The idea is that you can treat yourself occasionally without abandoning your dietary goals, and it will also help you not to feel that you are missing out. You can ignore this section if your symptoms are acute.

Breakfasts & Brunches

  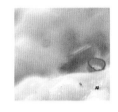   

These days there are many passing fads and fashions where food is concerned, all declaring that their approach is the best for optimum health and well-being. But there is no escaping from the simple truth—if you eat a good breakfast, it will keep you going right through the day and avoid the necessity to graze along the way. The following recipes are designed to do just that. All are quick and easy to prepare and suitable for the whole family. Choose, among others, from the traditional Bacon & Tomato Scramble, the refreshing Berry Smoothie, or the fragrant Fish Brunch. Whichever you choose, not only will it be extremely tasty but healthily sustaining.

  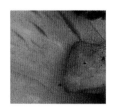 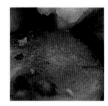 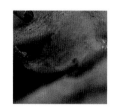 

serves 4

Bacon & Tomato Scramble

Ingredients

8 lean Canadian bacon slices

2 beefsteak or 4 tomatoes, halved

4 eggs

3 tbsp milk

salt and pepper

1 tbsp snipped fresh chives

1 tbsp unsalted butter

Nutritional Fact

Eggs contain lecithin, which helps break down fats in the liver, and sulfur, which helps to clear out toxins and alcohol from the liver.

Serving Analysis

- Calories   272
- Protein   16g
- Carbohydrate   6.9g
- Sugars   4.6g
- Fat   20.5g
- Saturates   7.5g
- GI   Low

1 Preheat the broiler to high and cover the broiler rack with foil. Arrange the bacon on the foil and cook under the preheated broiler for 3–4 minutes on each side, or until crisp. About 3 minutes before the end of cooking time, add the tomatoes, cut-side up, and cook for the remainder of the cooking time.

2 Meanwhile, beat the eggs, milk, and salt and pepper to taste in a medium-size bowl, then stir in the chives.

3 Melt the butter in a nonstick pan over medium heat, pour in the egg mixture, and cook, stirring gently with a wooden spoon, for 5–6 minutes, or until lightly set.

4 Arrange the egg scramble with the cooked bacon and tomatoes on warmed serving plates and serve at once. Sprinkle with extra snipped chives, if desired.

serves 1

Berry Smoothie

Nutritional Fact
Berries release their sugars very slowly and their dark color comes from protective bioflavonoids or plant chemicals, which are good for the circulation and heart health.

Serving Analysis

- *Calories*   272
- *Protein*   11g
- *Carbohydrate*   32g
- *Sugars*   24g
- *Fat*   12g
- *Saturates*   5g
- *GI*   Low

Ingredients

¹/₈ cup blueberries

³/₈ cup raspberries, thawed if frozen

1 tsp honey

scant 1 cup live or bio yogurt

about 1 heaping tbsp crushed ice

1 tbsp sesame seeds

1 Put the blueberries into a food processor or blender and process for 1 minute.

2 Add the raspberries, honey, and yogurt and process for an additional minute.

3 Add the ice and sesame seeds and process again for an additional minute.

4 Pour into a tall glass and serve at once.

serves 6

Nutty Cereal

Ingredients

generous ³/₄ cup shelled pecans, chopped

⁷/₈ cup shelled hazelnuts, chopped

1 cup slivered almonds

²/₃ cup no-soak dried apricots

³/₈ cup sunflower seeds

1¹/₄ cups rolled oats

To serve

freshly sliced banana

strawberries or raspberries

milk

1 Preheat the oven to 375°F/190°C. Spread all the nuts out on a baking sheet and toast in the preheated oven for 12–15 minutes, turning occasionally. Remove from the oven and let cool.

2 Meanwhile, finely chop the apricots.

3 Put all the ingredients into a large mixing bowl and mix together. Store in an airtight container.

4 When ready to serve, spoon 2–3 tablespoons into separate serving bowls, top with sliced banana, and a few strawberries or raspberries, then pour over a little milk and serve.

Nutritional Fact
Nuts, particularly almonds, are especially good for balancing blood sugar with good levels of most nutrients and omega-6 oils, the essential fatty acids.

Serving Analysis
- Calories   557
- Protein   16g
- Carbohydrate   32g
- Sugars   11g
- Fat   43.5g
- Saturates   3.7g
- GI   Low

serves 2

Piperade

Nutritional Fact

Red and orange bell peppers contain beta-carotene, a powerful antioxidant found in red, yellow, and orange fruit and vegetables.

Serving Analysis

- *Calories*   268
- *Protein*   15g
- *Carbohydrate*   15g
- *Sugars*   8.4g
- *Fat*   17g
- *Saturates*   3.2g
- *GI*   *Medium*

Ingredients

1 tbsp olive oil

1 onion, finely chopped

1–2 garlic cloves, crushed (optional)

1 red bell pepper, seeded and cut into thin strips

1 orange bell pepper, seeded and cut into thin strips

3 oz/85 g zucchini, coarsely grated

4 eggs

3 tbsp cold water

salt and pepper

1 tbsp chopped fresh basil

1 Heat the oil in a nonstick skillet over medium heat, add the onion, garlic, if using, and bell peppers, and cook, stirring frequently, for 5 minutes, or until softened. Stir in the zucchini.

2 Beat the eggs with the water and salt and pepper to taste in a medium-size bowl, then pour over the onion and bell pepper mixture. Using a fork or wooden spatula, gently draw the mixture from the edges of the skillet into the center, allowing the uncooked egg to flow to the edges of the skillet.

3 When the egg is lightly set, sprinkle the top with the basil, and cook for an additional 1–2 minutes, or until cooked to your personal preference.

4 Cut into wedges and serve at once.

serves 2–4 (2 as a light snack or 4 as part of a brunch)

Eggs Florentine

Ingredients

I lb/450 g fresh spinach leaves, rinsed

salt and pepper

2 oz/55 g unsalted butter

2 oz/55 g white mushrooms, sliced

³/₈ cup pine nuts, toasted

6 scallions, chopped

4 eggs

scant ¹/₄ cup all-purpose whole-wheat flour

1¹/₄ cups milk, warmed

I tsp prepared English mustard

3 oz/85 g sharp Cheddar cheese, grated

Nutritional Fact

Spinach has high levels of all minerals, but also folic acid, an important B vitamin needed for growth and healing. Folic acid is mainly found in leaves; in fact the name comes from the word "foliage."

Serving Analysis

• *Calories*	*432*
• *Protein*	*21g*
• *Carbohydrate*	*17g*
• *Sugars*	*6.1g*
• *Fat*	*32g*
• *Saturates*	*10.5g*
• *GI*	*Low*

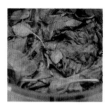

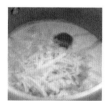

I Preheat the oven to 375°F/190°C. Shake off any excess water from the spinach, put into a large pan over medium heat with only the water clinging to the leaves, and sprinkle with a little salt. Cover and cook for 2–3 minutes, or until wilted. Drain, pressing out any excess liquid, then chop.

2 Heat I tablespoon of the butter in a small pan over medium heat, add the mushrooms, and cook for 2 minutes, stirring frequently. Add the pine nuts and scallions and cook for an additional 2 minutes. Remove, season to taste with salt and pepper, and sprinkle over the spinach. Set aside.

3 Meanwhile, fill a skillet with cold water and bring to a boil, then reduce the heat to a gentle simmer. Carefully break an egg into a cup and slip into the water. Add the remaining eggs and cook for 4–5 minutes, or until set. Carefully remove with a slotted spoon and arrange on top of the spinach mixture.

4 Melt the remaining butter in a pan and stir in the flour. Cook for 2 minutes, then remove from the heat and gradually stir in the milk. Return to the heat and cook, stirring constantly, until the mixture comes to a boil and has thickened. Stir in the mustard, then 2 oz/55 g of the cheese. Continue stirring until the cheese has melted. Add salt and pepper to taste, then pour over the eggs, completely covering them. Sprinkle with the remaining cheese.

5 Cook in the preheated oven for 20–25 minutes, or until piping hot and the top is golden brown and bubbling.

serves 4

Scrambled Eggs with Asparagus

Ingredients

2 oz/55 g unsalted butter
4 oz/115 g baby asparagus spears, diagonally sliced
3 oz/85 g button mushrooms, sliced
4 eggs
3 tbsp light cream
salt and pepper
4 thick slices cooked lean ham
1–2 tbsp snipped fresh chives

1 Melt half the butter in a skillet over medium heat, add the asparagus and mushrooms, and cook, stirring frequently, for 5 minutes, or until softened. Remove from the skillet, drain if necessary, and keep warm.

2 Beat the eggs with the cream and salt and pepper to taste in a medium-size bowl.

3 Melt the remaining butter in a nonstick pan over medium heat. Pour in the egg mixture and cook, stirring gently with a wooden spoon, for 5–6 minutes, or until lightly set.

4 Arrange the ham on serving plates, top with the asparagus and mushrooms, then the egg scramble. Sprinkle with the chives and serve at once.

Nutritional Fact
Asparagus is alkalizing, which means that it helps to clear the kidneys and is a good antidote for rich acidic foods such as meat and dairy.

Serving Analysis

• Calories	255
• Protein	16g
• Carbohydrate	3.7g
• Sugars	1.4g
• Fat	20g
• Saturates	10.4g
• GI	Low

serves 2–4 (2 for breakfast or 4 as part of a brunch)

Fluffy Shrimp Omelet

Ingredients

4 oz/115 g cooked shelled shrimp, thawed if frozen	4 eggs, separated
4 scallions, chopped	few dashes of Tabasco sauce, to taste
2 oz/55 g zucchini, grated	3 tbsp milk
	salt and pepper
	1 tbsp corn or olive oil
	1 oz/25 g sharp Cheddar cheese, grated

Nutritional Fact

Having a rich protein source such as shrimp for breakfast sets up the day for stable blood-sugar and energy release.

Serving Analysis

- *Calories*   157
- *Protein*   12g
- *Carbohydrate*   3.2g
- *Sugars*   2.3g
- *Fat*   11g
- *Saturates*   3.5g
- *GI*   Low

1 Pat the shrimp dry with paper towels, then mix with the scallions and zucchini in a bowl and set aside.

2 Using a fork, beat the egg yolks with the Tabasco, milk, and salt and pepper to taste in a separate bowl.

3 Whisk the egg whites in a large bowl until stiff, then gently stir the egg yolk mixture into the egg whites, taking care not to overmix.

4 Heat the oil in a large, nonstick skillet and when hot pour in the egg mixture. Cook over low heat for 4–6 minutes, or until lightly set. Preheat the broiler.

5 Spoon the shrimp mixture on top of the eggs and sprinkle with the cheese. Cook under the preheated broiler for 2–3 minutes, or until set and the top is golden brown. Cut into wedges and serve at once.

serves 4–6 (4 as a meal on its own or 6 as part of a brunch)

Fish Brunch

Ingredients

¹/₂ cup brown rice

salt and pepper

few saffron threads

10¹/₂ oz/300 g undyed smoked haddock fillets

1 bay leaf

1 large onion

²/₃ cup milk

4 oz/115 g green beans, chopped

2 tbsp olive oil

1–2 garlic cloves, crushed

²/₃ cup fish stock

scant ³/₄ cup corn kernels, thawed if frozen

2 tomatoes, chopped

8 oz/225 g raw jumbo shrimp, shelled

1 tbsp chopped fresh cilantro

1 Cook the rice in a pan of lightly salted boiling water with the saffron for 25 minutes, or until tender. Drain and set aside.

2 Meanwhile, rinse the haddock and put into a skillet with the bay leaf. Cut a few slices off the onion and add to the skillet. Pour over the milk and bring to a boil, then reduce the heat and let simmer for 10 minutes, or until the fish is cooked. Drain and let cool slightly. When cool enough to handle, remove and discard the skin and any remaining bones and flake the flesh into small pieces.

3 Cook the beans in a pan of lightly salted boiling water for 5 minutes, drain, then plunge into cold water. Drain again and set aside.

4 Finely chop the remaining onion. Heat the oil in a large skillet over medium heat, add the onion and garlic, and cook for 5 minutes, stirring frequently. Add the rice, stock, haddock, beans, corn, tomatoes, and jumbo shrimp. Cook, stirring occasionally, for 10 minutes, or until the shrimp are cooked and have turned pink. Add salt and pepper to taste, stir in the cilantro, and serve.

Nutritional Fact

Brown rice still contains the hulls that are removed in processing to make white rice; these provide B vitamins and fiber, which slow down the release of the starch into the bloodstream.

Serving Analysis
- *Calories*   *476*
- *Protein*   *38g*
- *Carbohydrate*   *56g*
- *Sugars*   *11.6g*
- *Fat*   *10.4g*
- *Saturates*   *0.8g*
- *GI*   *Low*

Soups & Light Meals

Whether you are looking for a speedy snack at lunch or suppertime or have to cater for an unexpected guest, you are sure to find something suitable and appetizing in this chapter. Most of the dishes take only a short time to prepare and cook, and if necessary can be prepared ahead of time and quickly cooked when required. Try the Chicken & Broccoli Soup, a hearty soup packed-full of chunky pieces of chicken, broccoli, and corn, or the Roasted Vegetable Salad—ideal for any occasion, served warm or cold. The Homemade Hummus and Tapenade are also easy and versatile options, making elegant appetizers as well as everyday snacks.

serves 4

Tomato & Bean Soup

Ingredients

1 tbsp olive oil
1 onion, chopped
2–3 garlic cloves, crushed
2 celery stalks, chopped
1 fresh red chili, seeded and chopped
1 tbsp tomato paste
4 cups vegetable stock
14 oz/400 g canned chopped tomatoes
7 oz/200 g canned red kidney beans, drained and rinsed
10¹/₂ oz/300 g canned cannellini beans, drained and rinsed
salt and pepper
generous 1¹/₄ cups cooked brown rice
1–2 tbsp chopped fresh basil
freshly grated Parmesan cheese (optional), to serve

Nutritional Fact

Beans are a fantastic source of vegetable protein and provide plenty of soluble fiber and B vitamins, which both help to regulate energy production and blood-sugar control.

Serving Analysis

- *Calories*   194
- *Protein*   8.3g
- *Carbohydrate*   31g
- *Sugars*   5.8g
- *Fat*   4.6g
- *Saturates*   0.6g
- *GI*   Low

1 Heat the oil in a large pan over medium heat, add the onion, garlic, celery, and chili, and cook for 3 minutes, stirring occasionally.

2 Blend the tomato paste with the stock and add to the pan with the tomatoes. Bring to a boil, then reduce the heat and let simmer for 10 minutes.

3 Add the beans and salt and pepper to taste and let simmer for an additional 10 minutes.

4 Stir in the rice and cook for an additional 5 minutes, or until all the ingredients are piping hot. Serve sprinkled with the basil and with Parmesan cheese, if desired.

serves 4

Laksa

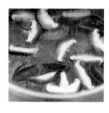

Ingredients

1 tbsp corn oil

2–3 garlic cloves, cut into thin slivers

1–2 fresh red Thai chilies, seeded and sliced

2 lemon grass stalks, outer leaves removed, chopped

1-inch/2.5-cm piece fresh gingerroot, grated

5 cups fish or vegetable stock

12 oz/350 g large raw shrimp, shelled and deveined

4 oz/115 g shiitake mushrooms, sliced

1 large carrot, grated

2 oz/55 g dried egg noodles (optional)

1–2 tsp Thai fish sauce

1 tbsp chopped fresh cilantro

1 Heat the oil in a large pan over medium heat, add the garlic, chilies, lemon grass, and ginger and cook for 5 minutes, stirring frequently. Add the stock and bring to a boil, then reduce the heat and let simmer for 5 minutes.

2 Stir in the shrimp, mushrooms, and carrot. If using the egg noodles, break into small lengths, add to the pan, and let simmer for an additional 5 minutes, or until the shrimp have turned pink and the noodles are tender.

3 Stir in the Thai fish sauce and cilantro and heat through for an additional minute before serving.

Nutritional Fact

Ginger gives this dish its curative properties and also improves digestion and circulation. It is anti-inflammatory and can help alleviate many common ailments.

Serving Analysis

• *Calories*	*157*
• *Protein*	*20g*
• *Carbohydrate*	*8.1g*
• *Sugars*	*2.1g*
• *Fat*	*5.2g*
• *Saturates*	*0.8g*
• *GI*	*Low*

serves 4

Smoky Fish & Bacon Cakes

Ingredients

10 oz/280 g undyed smoked haddock fillets, skinned

10 oz/280 g fresh haddock or cod fillets, skinned

$^2/_3$ cup milk

1 small onion, cut into thick slices

1 carrot, cut into thick slices

1 celery stalk, sliced

1 bay leaf

8 oz/225 g potatoes, peeled and cut into chunks

1 tbsp chopped fresh tarragon

1 tbsp finely grated lemon rind

salt and pepper

8 back bacon slices

1–2 tbsp corn oil

freshly cooked broccoli florets and broiled pepper wedges or fresh tomato sauce (see page 13), to serve

1 Remove and discard any remaining bones from the fish fillets, lightly rinse, and put into a large skillet with the milk, onion, carrot, celery, and bay leaf. Bring to a gentle boil, then reduce the heat and let simmer for 8–10 minutes, or until just cooked. Remove from the heat, let cool, then strain off the milk and set aside. When the fish is cool enough to handle, flake the flesh and set aside.

2 Meanwhile, cook the potatoes in a pan of lightly salted boiling water for 15 minutes, or until tender. Drain and mash, adding a little of the reserved milk to give a smooth but not sloppy consistency.

3 Add the fish with the tarragon, lemon rind, and salt and pepper to taste and mix together. Let cool.

4 Shape the mixture into 4 or 8 fish cakes and wrap 1 or 2 bacon slices around each fish cake. Cover and let chill in the refrigerator until required.

5 When ready to cook, heat the oil in a skillet over medium heat, add the fish cakes, and cook for 4–5 minutes on both sides, or until golden brown and piping hot. Drain and serve with cooked broccoli florets and broiled pepper wedges or tomato sauce.

Nutritional Fact
White fish contains good levels of vitamin A, which protects the eyes, liver, heart, and skin from damage from light, pollution, and toxins.

Serving Analysis
- Calories   397
- Protein   41g
- Carbohydrate   14g
- Sugars   4.4g
- Fat   19g
- Saturates   5.5g
- GI   Low

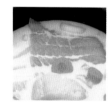  

serves 4–6

Chicken & Broccoli Soup

Ingredients

8 oz/225 g broccoli

salt and pepper

2 oz/55 g unsalted butter

1 onion, chopped

generous $^1/_8$ cup basmati rice

8 oz/225 g skinless, boneless chicken breast, cut into thin slivers

scant $^1/_4$ cup all-purpose whole-wheat flour

1 $^1/_4$ cups milk

2 cups chicken stock

generous $^1/_3$ cup corn kernels

Nutritional Fact

Broccoli is an absolute wonder food that increases liver function and also cleanses cells due to its high sulfur content.

Serving Analysis

• Calories	220
• Protein	15g
• Carbohydrate	16g
• Sugars	5.8g
• Fat	11g
• Saturates	6.5g
• GI	Low

1 Break the broccoli into small florets and cook in a pan of lightly salted boiling water for 3 minutes, drain, then plunge into cold water and set aside.

2 Melt the butter in a pan over medium heat, add the onion, rice, and chicken, and cook for 5 minutes, stirring frequently.

3 Remove the pan from the heat and stir in the flour. Return to the heat and cook for 2 minutes, stirring constantly. Stir in the milk and then the stock. Bring to a boil, stirring constantly, then reduce the heat and let simmer for 10 minutes.

4 Drain the broccoli and add to the pan with the corn and salt and pepper to taste. Let simmer for 5 minutes, or until the rice is tender, then serve.

serves 4

Cajun Chicken Salad

Ingredients

4 skinless, boneless chicken breasts, about 5 oz/140 g each

4 tsp Cajun seasoning

2 tsp corn oil (optional)

1 ripe mango, peeled, seeded, and cut into thick slices

7 oz/200 g mixed salad greens

1 red onion, thinly sliced and cut in half

6 oz/175 g cooked beet, diced

3 oz/85 g radishes, sliced

generous $^3/_8$ cup walnut halves

4 tbsp walnut oil

1–2 tsp Dijon mustard

1 tbsp lemon juice

salt and pepper

2 tbsp sesame seeds

1 Make 3 diagonal slashes across each chicken breast. Put the chicken into a shallow dish and sprinkle all over with the Cajun seasoning. Cover and let chill for at least 30 minutes.

2 When ready to cook, brush a stove-top grill pan with the corn oil, if using. Heat over high heat until very hot and a few drops of water sprinkled into the pan sizzle immediately. Add the chicken and cook for 7–8 minutes on each side, or until thoroughly cooked. If still slightly pink in the center, cook a little longer. Remove the chicken and set aside.

3 Add the mango slices to the pan and cook for 2 minutes on each side. Remove and set aside.

4 Meanwhile, arrange the salad greens in a salad bowl and sprinkle over the onion, beet, radishes, and walnut halves.

5 Put the walnut oil, mustard, lemon juice, and salt and pepper to taste in a screw-top jar and shake until well blended. Pour over the salad and sprinkle with the sesame seeds.

6 Arrange the mango and the salad on a serving plate and top with the chicken breast and a few of the salad greens.

Nutritional Fact
Beet helps stimulate the liver and cleans out toxins from the bowels.

Serving Analysis

- Calories   477
- Protein   38g
- Carbohydrate   23g
- Sugars   15g
- Fat   27g
- Saturates   2.9g
- GI   Low

serves 4

Creamy Leek Bake

Ingredients

2 oz/55 g unsalted butter, melted

generous 1 cup ground almonds

scant $^3/_8$ cup toasted chopped hazelnuts

$^1/_8$ cup sesame seeds

3 oz/85 g sharp Cheddar cheese, grated

1 tbsp virgin olive oil

12 oz/350 g leeks, thinly sliced

1 large red bell pepper, peeled, seeded, and cut into strips

1 orange bell pepper, peeled, seeded, and cut into strips

3 oz/85 g white mushrooms, sliced

scant 1 $^1/_4$ cups sour cream

1 tbsp chopped fresh oregano

salt and pepper

Nutritional Fact

Oregano is a member of the mint family and a potent natural antiseptic. It also aids digestion of heavy meals by calming the gut.

Serving Analysis

• Calories	691
• Protein	20g
• Carbohydrate	21g
• Sugars	5.7g
• Fat	62g
• Saturates	22g
• GI	Low

1 Preheat the oven to 375°F/190°C. Mix the butter, nuts, sesame seeds, and half the cheese together in a bowl. Press the mixture into the base of a 3^1/2-cup ovenproof gratin dish. Bake in the preheated oven for 15 minutes, or until the top is golden.

2 Meanwhile, heat the oil in a large skillet over medium heat, add the leeks, bell peppers, and mushrooms and cook for 5 minutes, stirring occasionally. Stir in the sour cream, oregano, and salt and pepper to taste.

3 Remove the nut base from the oven. Spread the sour cream mixture over the nut base and sprinkle with the remaining cheese. Bake in the oven for 15–20 minutes, or until the cheese is golden brown and bubbling.

serves 4

Roasted Vegetable Salad

Ingredients

1 onion

1 eggplant, about 8 oz/225 g

1 red bell pepper, seeded

1 orange bell pepper, seeded

1 large zucchini, about 6 oz/175 g

2–4 garlic cloves

2–4 tbsp olive oil

salt and pepper

1 tbsp balsamic vinegar

2 tbsp extra virgin olive oil

1 tbsp shredded fresh basil

freshly shaved Parmesan cheese, to serve

1 Preheat the oven to 400°F/200°C. Cut all the vegetables into even-size wedges, put into a roasting pan, and sprinkle over the garlic. Pour over 2 tablespoons of the olive oil and turn the vegetables in the oil until well coated. Add a little salt and pepper. Roast in the preheated oven for 40 minutes, or until tender, adding the extra olive oil if becoming too dry.

2 Meanwhile, put the vinegar, extra virgin olive oil, and salt and pepper to taste into a screw-top jar and shake until blended.

3 Once the vegetables are cooked, remove from the oven, arrange on a serving dish, and pour over the dressing. Sprinkle with the basil and serve with shavings of Parmesan cheese. Serve warm or cold.

Nutritional Fact

Roasting vegetables is a tasty way to eat the recommended five portions of vegetables and fruit per day. The benefits are heightened by including vegetables of different colors.

Serving Analysis

- *Calories*   216
- *Protein*   2.1g
- *Carbohydrate*   12g
- *Sugars*   6.4g
- *Fat*   18g
- *Saturates*   2.6g
- *GI*   Medium

makes 1 lb/450 g

Homemade Hummus

Ingredients

14 oz/400 g canned chickpeas, drained

2 tbsp sesame seed paste

4–6 tbsp virgin olive oil

4–6 tbsp lemon juice

2–3 garlic cloves, crushed

1–2 tbsp hot water

salt and pepper

red and orange bell pepper strips, celery stalks, and cucumber sticks, to serve

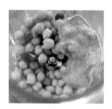 

1 Put all the ingredients (apart from the water and crudités) into a food processor and process to form a fairly smooth paste. Using the pulse button, slowly blend in the hot water to give a dipping consistency. Add salt and pepper to taste.

2 Spoon into a small serving dish, cover, and store in the refrigerator until required. Serve with the vegetable crudités.

Nutritional Fact

The high raw garlic content of these dips provides a high level of the compound allicin, which has antibacterial and heart protecting properties.

Analysis for Recipe

HUMMUS

• Calories	1326
• Protein	25.6g
• Carbohydrate	105g
• Sugars	20g
• Fat	90g
• Saturates	12.7g
• GI	Low

Analysis for Recipe

TAPENADE

• Calories	651
• Protein	17g
• Carbohydrate	20g
• Sugars	0.1g
• Fat	58g
• Saturates	3.3g
• GI	Low

makes 1 lb 2 oz/500 g

Homemade Tapenade

Ingredients

1 1/3 cups pitted black olives

3/8 cup capers, drained and rinsed if salty

2 garlic cloves, crushed

1 tbsp chopped fresh thyme

1 tsp Dijon mustard

2 oz/55 g canned anchovies, rinsed and patted dry

generous 1/3–1/2 cup virgin olive oil

1–2 tbsp brandy or hot water

pepper

2 tsp chopped fresh parsley, to garnish

red and orange bell pepper strips, celery stalks, and cucumber sticks, to serve

1 Put the olives, capers, garlic, thyme, mustard, and anchovies into a food processor and process until smooth. Using the pulse button, slowly blend in the oil until a thick purée is formed. Stir in the brandy or water and add pepper to taste.

2 Spoon into a small serving dish, cover, and store in the refrigerator until required. Serve, sprinkled with parsley, with the vegetable crudités.

Seafood, Meat & Poultry

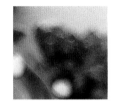

Here is a range of delicious main dishes that will satisfy the heartiest appetite, leaving you and your guests feeling full and energized. Choose from tender, succulent roast lamb served with a clean-tasting green salsa and sweet potato mash, garlic-scented angler fish cooked on a bed of roasted vegetables, or the comforting beef hotchpotch, thickened with nutritious pearl barley. Alternatively, sample turkey steaks marinated for added flavor and tenderness before being pan-grilled and served with a cannellini bean purée. Whichever dish you choose, it is sure to be a winner with both family and friends.

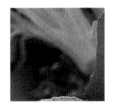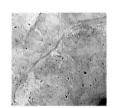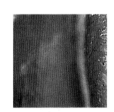

serves 4

Roasted Angler Fish

Ingredients

I lb 8 oz/675 g angler fish tail, skinned
4–5 large garlic cloves, peeled
salt and pepper
3 tbsp olive oil
I onion, cut into wedges
I small eggplant, about I0¹/₂ oz/300 g, cut into chunks
I red bell pepper, seeded, cut into wedges
I yellow bell pepper, seeded, cut into wedges
I large zucchini, about 8 oz/225 g, cut into wedges
I tbsp shredded fresh basil

 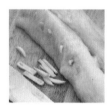 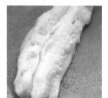

Nutritional Fact
Cooking in olive oil is the safest way to avoid damaged fats that can harm the body; olive oil is monounsaturated, which means it remains stable when heated to moderate temperatures.

Serving Analysis

• *Calories*	*289*
• *Protein*	*27g*
• *Carbohydrate*	*14g*
• *Sugars*	*7.2g*
• *Fat*	*13.5g*
• *Saturates*	*2.2g*
• *GI*	*Low*

I Preheat the oven to 400°F/200°C. Remove the central bone from the fish if not already removed and make small slits down each fillet. Cut 2 of the garlic cloves into thin slivers and insert into the fish. Place the fish on a sheet of waxed paper, season with salt and pepper to taste, and drizzle over I tablespoon of the oil. Bring the top edges together. Form into a pleat and fold over, then fold the ends underneath, completely encasing the fish. Set aside.

2 Put the remaining garlic cloves and all the vegetables into a roasting pan and sprinkle with the remaining oil, turning the vegetables so that they are well coated in the oil.

3 Roast in the preheated oven for 20 minutes, turning occasionally. Put the fish package on top of the vegetables and cook for an additional 15–20 minutes, or until the vegetables are tender and the fish is cooked.

4 Remove from the oven and open up the package. Cut the angler fish into thick slices. Arrange the vegetables on warmed serving plates, top with the fish slices, and sprinkle with the basil. Serve at once.

serves 4

Braised Seafood with Fennel

Ingredients

1 lb 4 oz/550 g assorted seafood such as salmon, cod, swordfish, large raw jumbo shrimp, and squid, cleaned

2 tbsp olive oil

1 onion, cut into wedges

1 fennel bulb, cut into thin wedges

14 oz/400 g canned chopped tomatoes

$^{2}/_{3}$ cup orange juice

1 tbsp finely grated orange rind

$^{1}/_{3}$ cup pitted black olives

salt and pepper

1 tbsp chopped fresh flatleaf parsley

fresh salad, such as baby spinach leaves, watercress, chicory, and orange segments, to serve

Nutritional Fact

Fennel contains volatile oils which help all aspects of digestion as they inhibit spasms in all smooth muscle, including the digestive tract, so reducing flatulence and bloating.

Serving Analysis

- Calories   476
- Protein   12g
- Carbohydrate   21g
- Sugars   7.8g
- Fat   39g
- Saturates   5.3g
- GI   Low

1 Prepare the seafood by removing and discarding any skin and bones from the fish and cutting into bite-size pieces. Shell and devein the shrimp. Cut the squid into thin slices or rings. Rinse all the fish and pat dry with paper towels.

2 Heat the oil in a large skillet over medium heat, add the onion and fennel, and cook, stirring occasionally, for 10 minutes, or until starting to soften. Add the tomatoes and orange juice and rind and bring to a boil, then reduce the heat and let simmer for 6–8 minutes.

3 Add the fish but not the shrimp or squid and let simmer for an additional 5 minutes before adding the remaining seafood and the olives. Cook for an additional 4–5 minutes, or until all the seafood is cooked and tender. Season to taste with salt and pepper, sprinkle with the parsley, and serve with a fresh salad.

Nutritional Fact

The garlic and cilantro help to stimulate digestion and encourage enzymes that help to break down the rich protein of the lamb.

Serving Analysis

• Calories   832
• Protein   43g
• Carbohydrate   13g
• Sugars   5.4g
• Fat   68g
• Saturates   22g
• GI   Low

serves 4

Pan-Fried Lamb Noisettes

1 First make the pesto. If using fresh or frozen fava beans, cook in a pan of lightly salted boiling water for 10 minutes, or until tender. Drain and put into a food processor with the garlic and cilantro. Using the pulse button, finely chop.

2 With the motor running, slowly pour in the extra virgin olive oil, ensuring that it is well blended. When all the oil has been incorporated, scrape the pesto into a bowl and add salt and pepper to taste and the Parmesan cheese. Spoon into a serving bowl, cover, and let chill in the refrigerator until required.

3 Meanwhile, arrange the eggplant slices on a large baking sheet and sprinkle with the olive oil, reserving 1 teaspoon, then sprinkle over the garlic and chili. Let stand for at least 30 minutes.

4 Preheat the broiler to medium and cover the broiler rack with foil. Arrange a single layer of eggplant slices on the broiler rack and cook under the preheated broiler for 3–5 minutes, turning once, until tender and starting to crisp. Remove and keep warm while cooking the remaining slices and lamb.

5 Meanwhile, preheat a nonstick skillet over medium heat. Season the lamb noisettes, add to the skillet, and brown on all sides, then cook for 6–8 minutes on each side, or until cooked to your personal preference.

6 Arrange 4 eggplant slices on each serving plate, top with the lamb, and serve, garnished with cilantro sprigs, with a spoonful of pesto.

Ingredients

1 large eggplant, cut into 16 slices

3 tbsp olive oil

3 large garlic cloves, crushed

1 fresh red jalapeño chili, seeded and finely chopped

8 lamb noisettes

salt and pepper

fresh cilantro sprigs

For the pesto

1 cup shelled fresh, frozen, or canned fava beans

salt and pepper

1 large garlic clove, crushed

1 tbsp chopped fresh cilantro

generous 1/3 cup extra virgin olive oil

1 1/2 tbsp freshly grated Parmesan cheese

serves 4

Crusted Rack of Lamb

1 Preheat the oven to 375°F/190°C. Wipe the lamb racks with paper towels and wrap the ends of the bones with foil.

2 Mix the bread crumbs, garlic, herbs, lemon rind, and salt and pepper to taste together in a bowl and bind with the egg. Press onto the skinned side of the lamb. Stand the racks in a roasting pan and roast in the preheated oven for 40–50 minutes, or until cooked to your personal preference.

3 Remove from the oven, remove and discard the foil from the bones, and cover with a sheet of foil. Let rest for 5 minutes.

4 Meanwhile, mix all the salsa ingredients together in a small serving bowl, cover, and set aside until required.

5 Cook the sweet potatoes in a pan of lightly salted boiling water for 15–20 minutes, or until tender when pierced with a fork. Drain, mash, then beat in the milk and mint until smooth.

6 Serve the lamb racks with the salsa and mash, accompanied by a lightly cooked green vegetable, such as broccoli.

Ingredients

2 racks of lamb, about 6–8 chops each, skin removed, trimmed of any excess fat

³/₄ cup fresh whole-wheat bread crumbs

2–3 garlic cloves, crushed

2 tbsp chopped fresh parsley

1 tbsp chopped fresh mint

1 tbsp finely grated lemon rind

salt and pepper

1 egg

lightly cooked green vegetable, such as broccoli, to serve

For the salsa

1 small green eating apple, washed, cored, and finely diced

2 tomatoes, seeded and finely diced

3 scallions, finely chopped

1 tbsp chopped fresh mint

For the mash

1 lb/450 g sweet potatoes, peeled and chopped

2 tbsp milk

1 tbsp chopped fresh mint

serves 4

Pan-Fried Lamb Noisettes

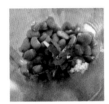  

1 First make the pesto. If using fresh or frozen fava beans, cook in a pan of lightly salted boiling water for 10 minutes, or until tender. Drain and put into a food processor with the garlic and cilantro. Using the pulse button, finely chop.

2 With the motor running, slowly pour in the extra virgin olive oil, ensuring that it is well blended. When all the oil has been incorporated, scrape the pesto into a bowl and add salt and pepper to taste and the Parmesan cheese. Spoon into a serving bowl, cover, and let chill in the refrigerator until required.

3 Meanwhile, arrange the eggplant slices on a large baking sheet and sprinkle with the olive oil, reserving 1 teaspoon, then sprinkle over the garlic and chili. Let stand for at least 30 minutes.

4 Preheat the broiler to medium and cover the broiler rack with foil. Arrange a single layer of eggplant slices on the broiler rack and cook under the preheated broiler for 3–5 minutes, turning once, until tender and starting to crisp. Remove and keep warm while cooking the remaining slices and lamb.

5 Meanwhile, preheat a nonstick skillet over medium heat. Season the lamb noisettes, add to the skillet, and brown on all sides, then cook for 6–8 minutes on each side, or until cooked to your personal preference.

6 Arrange 4 eggplant slices on each serving plate, top with the lamb, and serve, garnished with cilantro sprigs, with a spoonful of pesto.

Ingredients

1 large eggplant, cut into 16 slices

3 tbsp olive oil

3 large garlic cloves, crushed

1 fresh red jalapeño chili, seeded and finely chopped

8 lamb noisettes

salt and pepper

fresh cilantro sprigs

For the pesto

1 cup shelled fresh, frozen, or canned fava beans

salt and pepper

1 large garlic clove, crushed

1 tbsp chopped fresh cilantro

generous 1/3 cup extra virgin olive oil

1 1/2 tbsp freshly grated Parmesan cheese

serves 4

Crusted Rack of Lamb

1 Preheat the oven to 375°F/190°C. Wipe the lamb racks with paper towels and wrap the ends of the bones with foil.

2 Mix the bread crumbs, garlic, herbs, lemon rind, and salt and pepper to taste together in a bowl and bind with the egg. Press onto the skinned side of the lamb. Stand the racks in a roasting pan and roast in the preheated oven for 40–50 minutes, or until cooked to your personal preference.

3 Remove from the oven, remove and discard the foil from the bones, and cover with a sheet of foil. Let rest for 5 minutes.

4 Meanwhile, mix all the salsa ingredients together in a small serving bowl, cover, and set aside until required.

5 Cook the sweet potatoes in a pan of lightly salted boiling water for 15–20 minutes, or until tender when pierced with a fork. Drain, mash, then beat in the milk and mint until smooth.

6 Serve the lamb racks with the salsa and mash, accompanied by a lightly cooked green vegetable, such as broccoli.

Ingredients

2 racks of lamb, about 6–8 chops each, skin removed, trimmed of any excess fat

³/₄ cup fresh whole-wheat bread crumbs

2–3 garlic cloves, crushed

2 tbsp chopped fresh parsley

1 tbsp chopped fresh mint

1 tbsp finely grated lemon rind

salt and pepper

1 egg

lightly cooked green vegetable, such as broccoli, to serve

For the salsa

1 small green eating apple, washed, cored, and finely diced

2 tomatoes, seeded and finely diced

3 scallions, finely chopped

1 tbsp chopped fresh mint

For the mash

1 lb/450 g sweet potatoes, peeled and chopped

2 tbsp milk

1 tbsp chopped fresh mint

Nutritional Fact

Parsley and mint help the digestive process and sweet potatoes are a rich source of beta-carotene, which gives them their bright color and protects the body from UV damage from the sun.

Serving Analysis

- Calories   624
- Protein   42g
- Carbohydrate   43g
- Sugars   19g
- Fat   31g
- Saturates   14g
- GI   Low

serves 4

Beef & Bean Hotchpotch

Ingredients

2 tbsp olive oil

8 shallots, peeled

2 celery stalks, chopped

6 oz/175 g carrots, cut into chunks

1 lb 4 oz/550 g top round steak, trimmed of any visible fat and diced

1 tbsp all-purpose whole-wheat flour

1 tbsp tomato paste

2¹/₂ cups beef stock

generous ¹/₄ cup pearl barley, rinsed

salt and pepper

1 lb 4 oz/550 g sweet potatoes, peeled and sliced

1 tbsp chopped fresh parsley

Nutritional Fact

Celery is high in the chemical apigenin, which expands blood vessels and helps to prevent high blood pressure.

Serving Analysis

• *Calories*	*566*
• *Protein*	*48g*
• *Carbohydrate*	*52g*
• *Sugars*	*11g*
• *Fat*	*18g*
• *Saturates*	*3.7g*
• *GI*	*Low*

1 Preheat the oven to 350°F/180°C. Heat half the oil in a large pan over medium heat, add the shallots, celery, and carrots and cook for 2 minutes, stirring frequently. Add the steak and cook, stirring constantly, for 2–3 minutes, or until the meat is sealed on all sides.

2 Sprinkle in the flour and cook, stirring constantly, for 2 minutes. Blend the tomato paste with a little of the stock and stir into the pan, then stir in the remaining stock and the pearl barley. Bring to a boil, stirring constantly, then reduce the heat and let simmer for 5 minutes. Season to taste with salt and pepper and transfer to an ovenproof casserole dish.

3 Arrange the sweet potato slices on top and brush with the remaining oil. Bake in the preheated oven for 2–2¹/₂ hours, or until the meat and vegetables are tender. Remove the lid for the last 20 minutes of the cooking time to crisp the top. Sprinkle with the parsley before serving.

serves 4

Chicken with Bok Choy

Ingredients

6 oz/175 g broccoli

1 tbsp peanut oil

1-inch/2.5-cm piece fresh gingerroot, finely grated

1 fresh red Thai chili, seeded and chopped

2 garlic cloves, crushed

1 red onion, cut into wedges

1 lb/450 g skinless, boneless chicken breast, cut into thin strips

6 oz/175 g bok choy, shredded

4 oz/115 g baby corn, halved

1 tbsp light soy sauce

1 tbsp Thai fish sauce

1 tbsp chopped fresh cilantro

1 tbsp toasted sesame seeds

1 Break the broccoli into small florets and cook in a pan of lightly salted boiling water for 3 minutes. Drain and set aside.

2 Heat a wok over high heat until almost smoking, add the oil, and then add the ginger, chili, and garlic. Stir-fry for 1 minute. Add the onion and chicken and stir-fry for an additional 3–4 minutes, or until the chicken is sealed on all sides.

3 Add the remaining vegetables, including the broccoli, and stir-fry for 3–4 minutes, or until tender.

4 Add the soy and Thai fish sauces and stir-fry for an additional 1–2 minutes, then serve at once sprinkled with the cilantro and sesame seeds.

Nutritional Fact

Chicken is a source of complete protein, which, like all meats, means that it provides all the amino acids that help us to build body structures like skin, bones, and teeth. It has less saturated fat than red meat.

Serving Analysis

- Calories   233
- Protein   31g
- Carbohydrate   14g
- Sugars   4.8g
- Fat   6.6g
- Saturates   2.2g
- GI   Low

serves 4

Chicken Tagine

Ingredients

1 tbsp olive oil

1 onion, cut into small wedges

2–4 garlic cloves, sliced

1 lb/450 g skinless, boneless chicken breast, diced

1 tsp ground cumin

2 cinnamon sticks, lightly bruised

1 tbsp all-purpose whole-wheat flour

8 oz/225 g eggplant, diced

1 red bell pepper, seeded and chopped

3 oz/85 g white mushrooms, sliced

1 tbsp tomato paste

2¹/₂ cups chicken stock

10 oz/280 g canned chickpeas, drained and rinsed

¹/₃ cup no-soak dried apricots, chopped

salt and pepper

1 tbsp chopped fresh cilantro

1 Heat the oil in a large pan over medium heat, add the onion and garlic and cook for 3 minutes, stirring frequently. Add the chicken and cook, stirring constantly, for an additional 5 minutes, or until sealed on all sides. Add the cumin and cinnamon sticks to the pan halfway through sealing the chicken.

2 Sprinkle in the flour and cook, stirring constantly, for 2 minutes.

3 Add the eggplant, red bell pepper, and mushrooms and cook for an additional 2 minutes, stirring constantly.

4 Blend the tomato paste with the stock, stir into the pan, and bring to a boil. Reduce the heat and add the chickpeas and apricots. Cover and let simmer for 15–20 minutes, or until the chicken is tender.

5 Season with salt and pepper to taste and serve at once, sprinkled with cilantro.

Nutritional Fact
Chickpeas provide protein as well as calcium and iron and, like other legumes, have been shown to reduce cholesterol and glucose in the blood and are therefore good for the heart.

Serving Analysis
• Calories	313
• Protein	32g
• Carbohydrate	32g
• Sugars	13.5g
• Fat	6.2g
• Saturates	0.5g
• GI	Low

serves 4

Turkey Steaks with Bean Purée

Ingredients

4 turkey breast fillet steaks, about 5 oz/140 g each

1 tbsp red currant jelly

2 tbsp red wine vinegar

1 tbsp orange juice

fresh red currants, to garnish (optional)

freshly cooked green beans, tossed in butter, with 8 oz/225 g halved cherry tomatoes and 4 chopped scallions, to serve

For the bean purée

2 tbsp olive oil

1 lb 2 oz/500 g canned cannellini beans, drained, rinsed, and coarsely mashed

2–3 garlic cloves, crushed

1 tbsp chopped fresh mint

Nutritional Fact

Turkey is a good source of the amino acid or protein building block tryptophan, which the body makes into the neurotransmitter serotonin; this helps us sleep and feel content.

Serving Analysis

• Calories	400
• Protein	36g
• Carbohydrate	23g
• Sugars	3.7g
• Fat	17g
• Saturates	2.7g
• GI	Low

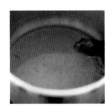

1 Wipe the turkey steaks with paper towels and put into a large, shallow dish. Heat the red currant jelly with the vinegar and orange juice in a small pan over low heat and stir until smooth. Pour over the turkey, cover, and let stand for at least 30 minutes.

2 When ready to cook, heat a stove-top grill pan over high heat until almost smoking. Add the turkey and cook for 5–6 minutes on each side, or until cooked.

3 Meanwhile, mix all the ingredients for the bean purée together in a bowl, transfer to a nonstick pan over low heat and heat through, stirring frequently, for 6–7 minutes, or until piping hot. Alternatively, transfer the mixture to a microwaveproof container, cover with plastic wrap, and heat in a 1,000-watt microwave oven for 3–4 minutes. Remove and let stand for 2 minutes. Remove and discard the plastic wrap and stir well.

4 Serve the turkey steaks on the bean purée with freshly cooked green beans, tossed in butter, with cherry tomatoes and scallions, garnished with red currants, if desired.

Vegetarian

These recipes are not just for vegetarians—they will appeal to all who enjoy exciting taste and texture combinations. The Gorgonzola & Vegetable Cheesecake offers a wonderful contrast of a crispy, nutty base and a creamy vegetable filling, while the Vegetable Biryani is bursting with aromatic flavors. Among other tasty fresh vegetables, such as portobello mushrooms and asparagus, broccoli features quite heavily, and for good reason. Not only is it flavorful and versatile, it also offers excellent health-promoting properties. Crammed full of the antioxidant vitamins beta-carotene and vitamin C, which are believed to help protect against cancer, it is also high in fiber with a low Glycemic Index.

   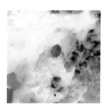 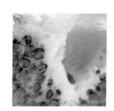 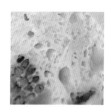

serves 4–6

Three Bean Salad

Ingredients

6 oz/175 g mixed salad greens, such as spinach, arugula, and frisée

1 red onion

3 oz/85 g radishes

6 oz/175 g cherry tomatoes

4 oz/115 g cooked beet

10 oz/280 g canned cannellini beans, drained and rinsed

7 oz/200 g canned red kidney beans, drained and rinsed

10¹/₂ oz/300 g canned flageolets, drained and rinsed

scant ¹/₃ cup dried cranberries

scant ¹/₂ cup roasted cashews

8 oz/225 g feta cheese (drained weight), crumbled

Nutritional Fact

Feta cheese made from goat's milk contains less of the milk sugar lactose than cheese made from cow's milk; this gives it its slightly bitter taste and makes it easier to digest.

Serving Analysis

• Calories	455
• Protein	17g
• Carbohydrate	37g
• Sugars	9.3g
• Fat	27g
• Saturates	9.5g
• GI	Low

For the dressing

4 tbsp extra virgin olive oil

1 tsp Dijon mustard

2 tbsp lemon juice

1 tbsp chopped fresh cilantro

salt and pepper

1 Arrange the salad greens in a salad bowl and set aside.

2 Thinly slice the onion, then cut in half to form half moons and put into a bowl.

3 Thinly slice the radishes, cut the tomatoes in half, and peel the beet if necessary and dice. Add to the onion with the remaining ingredients, except the nuts and cheese.

4 Put all the ingredients for the dressing into a screw-top jar and shake until blended. Pour over the bean mixture, toss lightly, then spoon on top of the salad greens.

5 Sprinkle over the nuts and cheese and serve at once.

serves 6

Gorgonzola & Vegetable Cheesecake

Ingredients

For the base

generous ¹/₂ cup ground almonds

1 cup fresh whole-wheat bread crumbs

scant ³/₈ cup finely chopped toasted hazelnuts

¹/₂ cup freshly grated Parmesan cheese

2 oz/55 g unsalted butter, melted

For the filling

1 tsp sun-dried tomatoes

4 oz/115 g baby asparagus spears

4 oz/115 g broccoli

salt and pepper

1 red bell pepper, peeled, seeded, and cut into thin strips

5 oz/140 g Gorgonzola cheese

1 lb/450 g mascarpone cheese

3 eggs

1 Preheat the oven to 350°F/180°C. Mix the almonds, bread crumbs, hazelnuts, and Parmesan cheese together in a bowl. Stir the butter into the nut mixture, mix well, then press into the base of an 8-inch/20-cm springform pan. Bake in the preheated oven for 15 minutes, then remove from the oven and set aside.

2 Meanwhile, put the tomatoes into a heatproof bowl and cover with almost boiling water. Let stand for 20 minutes, then drain and chop.

3 Trim the asparagus and, if thick, cut in half. Cut the broccoli into long, thin spears, including the stalk. Cook both together in a pan of lightly salted boiling water for 3 minutes, then drain, plunge into cold water, and let cool. Drain again.

4 Arrange the vegetables and red bell pepper over the nut base and crumble over half the Gorgonzola cheese.

5 Cream the mascarpone cheese in a bowl until soft, then gradually beat in the eggs. Continue beating until smooth. Pour over the vegetables and crumble the remaining Gorgonzola cheese over the top.

6 Put the pan on a baking sheet and bake in the preheated oven for 35–40 minutes, or until set.

7 Remove from the oven, release the pan, and remove the cheesecake.

Nutritional Fact
Using ground nuts instead of a grain for bases and other baking helps to reduce the carbohydrate content and slow down the release of sugars into the bloodstream.

Serving Analysis
- *Calories*   727
- *Protein*   23.2g
- *Carbohydrate*   16.3g
- *Sugars*   6.7g
- *Fat*   64.7g
- *Saturates*   8g
- *GI*   Low

serves 6–8

Nutty Stilton Roast

1 Preheat the oven to 350°F/180°C. Lightly oil a 2-lb/900-g loaf pan.

2 Finely chop one of the onions. Heat 1 tablespoon of the oil in a skillet over medium heat, add the chopped onion, 1–2 of the garlic cloves, and the celery and cook for 5 minutes, stirring occasionally.

3 Remove from the skillet, drain through a strainer and transfer to a food processor with the nuts, bread crumbs, half the cheese, and the basil. Using the pulse button, blend the ingredients together, then slowly blend in the egg to form a stiff mixture. Season to taste with salt and pepper.

4 Cut the remaining onion into thin wedges. Heat the remaining oil in a skillet over medium heat, add the onion, remaining garlic, red bell pepper, and zucchini and cook for 5 minutes, stirring frequently. Remove from the skillet, add salt and pepper to taste, and drain through a strainer.

5 Place half the nut mixture in the prepared pan and smooth the surface. Arrange the onion and bell pepper mixture on top and crumble over the remaining cheese. Top with the remaining nut mixture and press down firmly. Cover with foil.

6 Bake in the preheated oven for 45 minutes. Remove the foil and bake for an additional 25–35 minutes, or until cooked and firm to the touch.

7 Remove from the oven and let cool for 5 minutes before inverting onto a warmed serving platter. Serve with a little of the tomato sauce drizzled over the top, garnished with basil sprigs and cherry tomatoes, accompanied by a green salad or vegetables.

Ingredients

2 tbsp virgin olive oil, plus extra for oiling

2 onions

3–5 garlic cloves, crushed

2 celery stalks, finely sliced

scant 1 cup cooked and peeled chestnuts

generous 1 cup mixed chopped nuts

generous 1/2 cup ground almonds

1 cup fresh whole-wheat bread crumbs

8 oz/225 g Stilton cheese, crumbled

1 tbsp chopped fresh basil, plus extra sprigs to garnish

1 egg, beaten

salt and pepper

1 red bell pepper, peeled, seeded, and cut into thin wedges

1 zucchini, about 4 oz/115 g, cut into wedges

cherry tomatoes, to garnish

To serve

quick tomato sauce (see page 13)

green salad or lightly cooked vegetables

Nutritional Fact

Chestnuts are virtually fat free and higher in complex carbohydrates than other nuts; in fact nutritionally they are similar to brown rice.

Serving Analysis

• Calories	462
• Protein	17g
• Carbohydrate	33g
• Sugars	7.5g
• Fat	29.5g
• Saturates	9.5g
• GI	Low

serves 4

Baked Portobello Mushrooms

Ingredients

4 large portobello mushrooms

7 oz/200 g canned red kidney beans, drained and rinsed

4 scallions, chopped

1 fresh red jalapeño chili, seeded and finely chopped

1 tbsp finely grated lemon rind

1 tbsp chopped fresh flatleaf parsley, plus extra sprigs to garnish

salt and pepper

3 oz/85 g zucchini, coarsely grated

3 oz/85 g carrots, coarsely grated

$^3/_8$ cup pine nuts, toasted

generous $^1/_4$ cup raisins

1$^1/_4$ cups vegetable stock

For the sauce

$^2/_3$ cup strained plain yogurt

1 tbsp chopped fresh parsley, plus extra to garnish

1 tbsp grated lemon rind

salt and pepper

asparagus and bell pepper stir-fry, to serve (optional)

Nutritional Fact

Many studies have been done on mushrooms and their abilities to enhance the immune system and feed the good bacteria in the gut; they are also high in minerals and protein.

Serving Analysis

• *Calories*	*214*
• *Protein*	*10g*
• *Carbohydrate*	*27g*
• *Sugars*	*13.3g*
• *Fat*	*8.8g*
• *Saturates*	*2g*
• *GI*	*Low*

1 Preheat the oven to 350°F/180°C. Peel the mushrooms and carefully remove the stalks. Trim and rinse the stalks.

2 Put the beans, mushroom stalks, scallions, chili, lemon rind, parsley, and salt and pepper to taste into a food processor and process for 2 minutes.

3 Scrape the mixture into a bowl and add the zucchini, carrots, pine nuts, and raisins. Mix well and use to stuff the mushroom cups.

4 Arrange the stuffed mushrooms in an ovenproof dish, pour round the stock, and cover with foil. Bake in the preheated oven for 30 minutes, removing the foil for the last 10 minutes of the cooking time.

5 Meanwhile, to make the sauce, blend all the ingredients together in a small serving dish.

6 Serve the mushrooms hot with the sauce, garnished with parsley sprigs and accompanied by an asparagus and bell pepper stir-fry, if desired.

serves 6

Vegetable Pot

Ingredients

2 tbsp olive oil

8 pearl onions, peeled

2 celery stalks, sliced

8 oz/225 g carrots, thickly sliced

8 oz/225 g turnips, diced

generous ¹/₄ cup pearl barley, rinsed

3–3¹/₂ cups vegetable stock

salt and pepper

12 oz/350 g diced Quorn®

³/₄ cup partially thawed frozen peas

1 tbsp chopped fresh parsley,
to garnish

Nutritional Fact

*Peas are actually a
legume or bean, not a
vegetable, and as such
contain the chemical
genistein, which studies
have shown helps to
guard against cancer.*

Serving Analysis

- *Calories*   *334*
- *Protein*   *50g*
- *Carbohydrate*   *26g*
- *Sugars*   *8.2g*
- *Fat*   *7g*
- *Saturates*   *0.3g*
- *GI*   *Medium*

1 Preheat the oven to 350°F/180°C. Heat half the oil in a large pan or ovenproof casserole dish over medium heat, add the onions, celery, carrots, and turnips, and cook for 10 minutes, stirring frequently. Add the pearl barley and cook for 1 minute, stirring occasionally, then pour in the stock and bring to a boil.

2 Season to taste with salt and pepper and cover. Cook in the preheated oven for 1–1¹/₄ hours.

3 Meanwhile, heat the remaining oil in a skillet over medium heat, add the Quorn®, and cook, stirring frequently, for 5–8 minutes, or until golden.

4 Add the Quorn® to the casserole with the peas and cook for an additional 10–20 minutes, or until the vegetables are tender. Taste and adjust the seasoning and serve sprinkled with parsley.

serves 4

Vegetable Biryani

Ingredients

2 tbsp vegetable oil

3 whole cloves

3 cardamom pods, cracked

1 onion, chopped

4 oz/115 g carrots, chopped

2–3 garlic cloves, crushed

1–2 fresh red chilies, seeded and chopped

1-inch/2.5-cm piece fresh gingerroot, grated

4 oz/115 g cauliflower, broken into small florets

6 oz/175 g broccoli, broken into small florets

4 oz/115 g green beans, chopped

14 oz/400 g canned chopped tomatoes

2/3 cup vegetable stock

salt and pepper

4 oz/115 g okra, sliced

1 tbsp chopped fresh cilantro, plus extra sprigs to garnish

generous 1/4 cup brown basmati rice

few saffron threads (optional)

zested lime rind, to garnish

1 Heat the oil in a large pan over low heat, add the spices, onion, carrots, garlic, chilies, and ginger and cook, stirring frequently, for 5 minutes.

2 Add all the vegetables, except the okra, and cook, stirring frequently, for 5 minutes. Stir in the tomatoes, stock, and salt and pepper to taste and bring to a boil. Reduce the heat, cover, and let simmer for 10 minutes.

3 Add the okra and cook for an additional 8–10 minutes, or until the vegetables are tender. Stir in the cilantro. Strain off any excess liquid and keep warm.

4 Meanwhile, cook the rice with the saffron in a pan of lightly salted boiling water for 25 minutes, or until tender. Drain and keep warm.

5 Layer the vegetables and cooked rice in a deep dish or ovenproof bowl, packing the layers down firmly. Let stand for about 5 minutes, then invert onto a warmed serving dish and serve, garnished with zested lime rind and cilantro sprigs, with the reserved liquid.

Nutritional Fact

Cauliflower is a great source of vitamin B$_6$, which is needed for energy production, blood-sugar balance, correct hormone balance and good mental health and mood.

Serving Analysis

- Calories   346
- Protein   12.5g
- Carbohydrate   59g
- Sugars   14.5g
- Fat   8.9g
- Saturates   1.1g
- GI   Medium

serves 4

Baby Corn with Dal

Ingredients

generous 1 cup red split lentils

2 tbsp vegetable oil

1 tsp cumin seeds

1 tsp ground coriander

$^1/_2$ tsp asafetida

1 fresh red chili, seeded and finely chopped

4 oz/115 g green beans, chopped, blanched, and drained

1 green bell pepper, seeded and chopped

4 oz/115 g baby corn, diagonally sliced

$^2/_3$ cup vegetable stock

2 tomatoes, seeded and chopped

1 tbsp chopped fresh cilantro

1 tbsp poppy seeds

Nutritional Fact

Cumin contains 11 chemicals with antibacterial action, which means that it helps to ward off infection and also promotes good body odor.

Serving Analysis

• Calories	418
• Protein	22g
• Carbohydrate	62g
• Sugars	9.6g
• Fat	10.3g
• Saturates	1.4g
• GI	Low

1 Rinse the lentils 2–3 times in cold water. Put into a large pan and cover with cold water. Bring to a boil, then reduce the heat and let simmer for 15–20 minutes, or until tender. Drain, return to the pan, and keep warm.

2 Meanwhile, heat the oil in a separate pan over low heat, add the spices, and chili and cook for 2 minutes, stirring constantly. Add the beans, green bell pepper, and baby corn and cook for 2 minutes, stirring constantly.

3 Stir in the stock and bring to a boil, then reduce the heat and let simmer for 5 minutes, or until the vegetables are just tender.

4 Stir the vegetables and their liquid into the cooked lentils with the tomatoes and heat through for 5–8 minutes, or until piping hot.

5 Serve at once sprinkled with the fresh cilantro and poppy seeds.

serves 2–4 (2 as a light supper or 4 as part of a buffet)

Broccoli & Sesame Frittata

 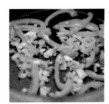 

1 Cook the broccoli in a pan of lightly salted boiling water for 4 minutes. Add the asparagus after 2 minutes. Drain, then plunge into cold water. Drain again and set aside.

2 Heat the oil in a large skillet over low heat, add the onion, garlic, and orange bell pepper and cook, stirring frequently, for 8 minutes, or until the vegetables have softened.

3 Beat the eggs with the water and salt and pepper to taste in a medium-size bowl. Pour into the skillet, add the broccoli and asparagus, and stir gently. Cook over medium heat for 3–4 minutes, drawing the mixture from the edges of the skillet into the center, allowing the uncooked egg to flow to the edges of the skillet. Preheat the broiler.

4 Sprinkle the top of the frittata with the sesame seeds and cheese and cook under the preheated broiler for 3–5 minutes, or until golden and set. Sprinkle with the scallions, cut into wedges, and serve. Serve either warm or cold.

Ingredients

6 oz/175 g broccoli, broken into small florets

salt and pepper

3 oz/85 g asparagus spears, diagonally sliced

1 tbsp virgin olive oil

1 onion, cut into small wedges

2–4 garlic cloves, finely chopped

1 large orange bell pepper, seeded and chopped

4 eggs

3 tbsp cold water

1/8 cup sesame seeds

1/8 cup freshly grated Parmesan cheese

3 scallions, finely sliced

Nutritional Fact
Sesame seeds are one of the richest sources of phytosterols, plant chemicals that can be absorbed into the bloodstream and remove the cholesterol that has built up there.

Serving Analysis

- *Calories*   415
- *Protein*   26g
- *Carbohydrate*   19g
- *Sugars*   10g
- *Fat*   27g
- *Saturates*   6.5g
- *GI*   Low

Desserts & Baking

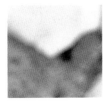

Everyone needs a treat or two occasionally, so when you are looking for one, turn immediately to this chapter. These desserts and sweet snacks are sure to tempt and delight but you can enjoy them safe in the knowledge that they are not heavily laden with undesirable sugar-rich carbohydrates.

Try the colorful Raspberry Ripple Ice Cream, which is really easy to make, or the moist Carrot Bars, ideal for lunch boxes or as an occasional afternoon-tea treat. For special occasions, everyone will be impressed by the elegant and incredibly fruity Apple & Elderberry Flower Dessert and suitably fooled by the sumptuous Cheat's Crème Brûlée!

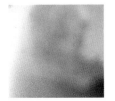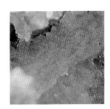

serves 6

Raspberry Ripple Ice Cream

Ingredients

3/8 cup fresh or frozen raspberries, thawed if frozen, plus extra to serve

2 tbsp water

2 eggs

1 tbsp superfine sugar

1¼ cups milk, warmed

1 tsp vanilla extract

1¼ cups heavy cream

Nutritional Fact

Raspberries are known as a good remedy for diarrhea. When eaten with their seeds intact, they provide many important enzymes and nutrients that we need for energy production.

Serving Analysis

- Calories   239
- Protein   4.9g
- Carbohydrate   8g
- Sugars   6.9g
- Fat   21g
- Saturates   12.6g
- GI   Low

1 Turn the freezer to rapid. Put the raspberries into a pan with the water and bring to a boil, then reduce the heat and let simmer gently for 5 minutes. Remove from the heat and let cool for 30 minutes.

2 Transfer to a food processor or blender and process to a purée, then rub through a nylon strainer to remove the pips. Set aside.

3 Beat the eggs in a bowl. Stir the sugar into the warmed milk, then slowly pour onto the eggs, beating constantly. Strain into a clean pan and cook over low heat, stirring constantly, for 8–10 minutes, or until the custard thickens and coats the back of a wooden spoon. Add the vanilla extract, remove from the heat, and let cool.

4 Half-whip the cream in a large bowl, then slowly stir in the cooled custard. Pour into a freezerproof container and freeze for 1½ hours, or until starting to set around the outside. Remove from the freezer and stir the mixture, breaking up any ice crystals.

5 Return the mixture to the freezer and freeze for an additional hour, then remove from the freezer and gently stir in the raspberry purée to give a rippled effect. Return to the freezer for an additional hour or until frozen. Serve in scoops with extra fresh raspberries.

serves 4–6

Cheat's Crème Brûlée

Ingredients

1–scant 1 1/3 cups mixed soft fruits, such as blueberries and pitted fresh cherries

1 1/2–2 tbsp Cointreau or orange flower water

1 1/8 cups mascarpone cheese

scant 1 cup sour cream

2–3 tbsp brown sugar

1 Prepare the fruit, if necessary, and lightly rinse, then place in the bases of 4–6 x 2/3-cup ramekins. Sprinkle the fruit with the Cointreau or orange flower water.

2 Cream the cheese in a bowl until soft, then gradually beat in the sour cream.

3 Spoon the cheese mixture over the fruit, smoothing the surface and ensuring that the tops are level. Let chill in the refrigerator for at least 2 hours.

4 Sprinkle the tops with the sugar. Using a chef's blowtorch, broil the tops until caramelized (about 2–3 minutes). Alternatively, cook under a preheated broiler, turning the dishes, for 3–4 minutes, or until the tops are lightly caramelized all over.

5 Serve at once or let chill in the refrigerator for 15–20 minutes before serving.

Nutritional Fact

The blue pigment in blueberries is a type of anthocyadin and is a powerful liver protector; like cranberries they also help prevent urinary infections.

Serving Analysis

- *Calories*   356
- *Protein*   4.4g
- *Carbohydrate*   18g
- *Sugars*   16g
- *Fat*   30g
- *Saturates*   21.6g
- *GI*   *Medium*

makes 12 cups

Apricot & Yogurt Cups

Ingredients

2¹/₂ cups plain yogurt

few drops of almond extract

2–3 tsp honey, warmed

scant ¹/₂ cup whole blanched almonds

1 cup no-soak dried apricots

Nutritional Fact

Apricots contain good amounts of fiber and are famed for clearing out the bowel and therefore the body; try to buy the unsulfured variety of these and all dried fruits to avoid stomach upsets.

Serving Analysis

- Calories   88
- Protein   3.4g
- Carbohydrate   10.5g
- Sugars   10g
- Fat   3.7g
- Saturates   1g
- GI   Low

1 Line a 12-cup bun pan with small paper cake cases.

2 Spoon the yogurt into a mixing bowl, add the almond extract and honey, and stir well.

3 Using a small, sharp knife, cut the almonds into very thin slivers and stir into the yogurt mixture.

4 Using a pair of kitchen scissors, cut the apricots into small pieces, then stir into the yogurt.

5 Spoon the mixture into the paper cases and freeze for 1¹/₂–2 hours, or until just frozen. Serve at once.

serves 6

Aromatic Pears

Ingredients

2 tbsp honey

2 cups cold water

2 whole star anise

1 cinnamon stick, lightly bruised, plus extra to decorate (optional)

4 whole cloves

4-inch/10-cm strip of thinly pared orange rind

6 semiripe pears

1 1/4 cups strained plain yogurt

1 tbsp orange juice

2 tsp finely grated orange rind

1/2–1 tsp ground cinnamon

Nutritional Fact

Pears, like apples, contain pectin, a type of fiber that slows down the release of sugar after meals, removes unwanted toxins, and helps lower cholesterol.

Serving Analysis

• Calories	162
• Protein	2.8g
• Carbohydrate	35g
• Sugars	26g
• Fat	2.6g
• Saturates	1.1g
• GI	Low

1 Put the honey, water, spices, and thinly pared orange rind into a large pan or skillet over low heat and heat, stirring, until the honey has dissolved. Bring to a boil and boil gently for 5 minutes, then reduce the heat and let simmer while peeling the pears.

2 Thinly peel the pears, keeping the stalks in place, and add to the syrup. Add to the pan, cover, and cook over low heat, turning the fruit occasionally, for 15–20 minutes, or until the pears are tender when gently pierced with a small, sharp knife. Remove from the heat, keep covered with the lid or a large piece of foil, and leave until cool—about 1 hour—turning the pears occasionally in the syrup.

3 Meanwhile, blend the yogurt with the orange juice and rind and cinnamon in a serving bowl, cover, and let chill in the refrigerator until required.

4 Serve the pears, with some of the syrup poured over, with the yogurt. Decorate with cinnamon sticks, if desired.

serves 6–8

Apple & Elderberry Flower Dessert

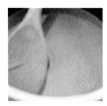

Nutritional Fact
Honey is a sugar essentially made from flowers and has a lower GI value than sugar. Choose one from a single source rather then a blended variety and you will benefit from its healing properties.

Serving Analysis
- Calories   74
- Protein   1.8g
- Carbohydrate   17g
- Sugars   14g
- Fat   0.01g
- Saturates   0.0g
- GI   Medium

Ingredients

2 cups apple and elderberry flower fruit juice

1–2 tbsp honey

¼ oz/11 g sachet gelatin

3 tbsp Cointreau or brandy, or extra fruit juice

1 lb/450 g fruit, such as galia and ogen melon and green and red seedless grapes

1 Put the fruit juice into a medium-size pan. Stir in the honey, then sprinkle the gelatin over the surface. Place over low heat and slowly bring to a boil, whisking constantly with a balloon whisk. When the mixture is just boiling, remove from the heat and let cool at room temperature for 3–4 hours until it starts to set.

2 Meanwhile, prepare the fruit. If using melons, cut into slices, remove and discard the seeds and skin, then cut the flesh into small pieces. If using grapes, wash and dry thoroughly and remove from the stalks. Cut in half if large. Set aside.

3 Once the gelatin is starting to set, stir the prepared fruit into the gelatin and then spoon carefully into either a glass serving bowl or individual glass serving dishes or wine glasses.

4 Let set in the refrigerator for about 2 hours, then serve.

serves 4

Iced Raspberry Sundae

Ingredients

1 lb/450 g fresh raspberries, plus extra to decorate

2 cups heavy cream

$^1/_2$ cup slivered almonds

1$^1/_4$ cups fresh pitted or canned cherries

$^1/_2$ oz/15 g semisweet chocolate, coarsely grated

fresh mint sprigs, to garnish

1 Preheat the oven to 400°F/200°C. Set aside $^1/_2$ cup of the raspberries and lightly crush the remainder.

2 Whip the cream in a medium-size bowl until soft peaks form. Put 4 tablespoons of the cream into a small bowl, cover, and set aside. Stir the crushed raspberries into the remaining cream, spoon into a freezerproof container, and freeze for 1 hour, or until partially frozen.

3 Meanwhile, spread the almonds out on a baking sheet and toast in the preheated oven, turning occasionally, for 8–10 minutes, or until golden brown. Remove from the oven and let cool.

4 Arrange the reserved raspberries and cherries in the bases of 4 sundae glasses, then sprinkle with a few toasted almonds. Cover with scoops of the frozen raspberry mixture, then either pipe or swirl the reserved cream on top. Sprinkle with the grated chocolate and decorate with extra raspberries and mint sprigs.

Nutritional Fact
Semisweet chocolate contains chemicals called catechins, which are potent antioxidants and protect the body against damage and disease.

Serving Analysis

• Calories	597
• Protein	7.2g
• Carbohydrate	26g
• Sugars	18g
• Fat	54g
• Saturates	29g
• GI	Low

makes 9 squares

Fruit & Nut Squares

Nutritional Fact

Oats release their sugars very slowly and have a low GI value; they have an excellent ability to normalize blood sugar and their fat content creates heat in the body.

Serving Analysis

- Calories   296
- Protein   6.7g
- Carbohydrate   22g
- Sugars   13.3g
- Fat   22g
- Saturates   7.6g
- GI   Low

1 Preheat the oven to 350°F/180°C. Lightly grease a 7-inch/18-cm shallow, square baking pan with butter. Beat the remaining butter with the honey in a bowl until creamy, then beat in the egg with the almonds.

2 Add the remaining ingredients and mix together. Press into the prepared pan, ensuring that the mixture is firmly packed. Smooth the top.

3 Bake in the preheated oven for 20–25 minutes, or until firm to the touch and golden brown.

4 Remove from the oven and let stand for 10 minutes before marking into squares. Let stand until cold before removing from the pan. Store in an airtight container.

Ingredients

4 oz/115 g unsalted butter, plus extra for greasing

2 tbsp honey

1 egg, beaten

scant $^7/_8$ cup ground almonds

$^7/_8$ cup no-soak dried apricots, finely chopped

$^1/_3$ cup dried cherries

scant $^3/_8$ cup toasted chopped hazelnuts

$^1/_8$ cup sesame seeds

scant 1 cup rolled oats

makes 14–16 bars

Carrot Bars

 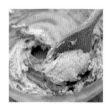 

Ingredients

corn oil, for oiling

6 oz/175 g unsalted butter

generous $^3/_8$ cup (packed) brown sugar

2 eggs, beaten

scant $^1/_2$ cup self-rising whole-wheat flour, sifted

1 tsp baking powder, sifted

1 tsp ground cinnamon, sifted

generous $1^1/_8$ cups ground almonds

4 oz/115 g carrot, coarsely grated

$^1/_2$ cup golden raisins

$^1/_2$ cup no-soak dried apricots, finely chopped

scant $^3/_8$ cup toasted chopped hazelnuts

1 tbsp slivered almonds

Nutritional Fact

Cinnamon helps the body to use insulin more effectively by helping fat cells recognize and respond to it; cooking does not affect its potency.

Serving Analysis

• Calories	234
• Protein	4.2g
• Carbohydrate	19.5g
• Sugars	13.5g
• Fat	17g
• Saturates	6.7g
• GI	Medium

1 Preheat the oven to 350°F/180°C. Lightly oil and line a 10- x 8-inch/25- x 20-cm shallow, rectangular baking pan with nonstick parchment paper.

2 Cream the butter and sugar together in a bowl until light and fluffy, then gradually beat in the eggs, adding a little flour after each addition.

3 Add all the remaining ingredients, except the slivered almonds. Spoon the mixture into the prepared pan and smooth the top. Sprinkle with the slivered almonds.

4 Bake in the preheated oven for 35–45 minutes, or until the mixture is cooked and a skewer inserted into the center comes out clean.

5 Remove from the oven and let cool in the pan. Remove from the pan, discard the lining paper, and cut into bars.

Index